The LEGEND of DESPERATE DAN

TO generations of British children over the last sixty years, mention of Cactusville, Aunt Aggie and, in particular, cow-pie, can mean only one thing — Desperate Dan — the roughest, toughest cowboy you'll ever set eyes on.

With his great barrel chest and distinctive jutting, unshaven chin, Dan has become one of the best loved and most recognisable characters in British comic history since he first appeared in The Dandy in 1937 alongside front cover star, Korky the Cat and arch-peeper, Keyhole Kate.

The artist, selected by Editor Albert Barnes, for the task of drawing Dan was Dudley D. Watkins, who had been drawing The Broons and Oor Wullie for The Sunday Post Fun Section with great success since the previous year.

Eventually, Albert's own chin was used as the model for Dan's now famous jaw, which Albert described as looking like a "chest of drawers".

Issue 1 of the Dandy featuring Korky the Cat and Keyhole Kate. Danny and Katy and Dog-Ears Montana arrived later.

Dan made his debut in issue 1 of The Dandy, dated 4th December, 1937. In those days Dan was given a humble half page but this story set the tone for what would follow. Dan buys a horse which collapses under his enormous weight a mile out of town, so Dan carries the unfortunate horse back to town and socks the dealer for selling him a dud.

Dan quickly proved to be a hit and in 1939 he was promoted first to two-thirds of a page then, later in the same year, to a full page. Not bad for a cowpoke from Cactusville.

In the following years, Dan's character developed and new characters joined the strip. First to arrive was Aunt Aggie, followed by Granny, Dan's nephew and niece, Danny and Katey, along with the Mayor, Dog-Ears Montana and later, the Sheriff. When Aunt Aggie arrived in Cactusville, she brought with her something which would be almost as much a part of the Desperate Dan legend as Dan himself — Dan's favourite food, cow-pie.

Dan's strength also continued to grow, until he eventually won the World's Strongest Man contest, though the title had never been in doubt. Who could compete with a man who had lifted elephants in one hand, pulled steam-trains and even held a battleship out of the water while it was repaired?

Dan's adventures weren't contained solely to Cactusville, or even the Wild West. In particular during the Second World

Aunt Aggie and her most famous creation.

YOU CAN HELP BRITAIN BY COLLECTING WASTE-PAPER

Albert Barnes, The Dandy Editor from 1937-1982 made a fleeting appearance in a 1946 Desperate Dan strip.

A rare meeting of two comic legends. Desperate Dan as drawn by Oor Wullie.

EVENING FLAIL
ABE BARNES Editor

ROOND the Chest 80 INCHES

ROOND The ARMS 30 inches

ROOND THE LEG

AN' HE'LL BE ABOOT FIFTY INCHES ROOND THE LEG!

encouraging his young readers to save waste paper.

The war may have ended in 1945 but Desperate Dan's pages were anything but peaceful. He continued his adventures in his own robust fashion and it was in this post-war period that some of the Dan stories became serials, often spread over several months. The split of serials and single issue stories was roughly equal, and this trend continued until the late 1950s when the serials were phased out. Through the 1960s Cactusville continued to be the weirdest town in the West, with London buses, post boxes and British bobbies side by side with a Western sheriff, cowboys and the stagecoach. Each week Dan appeared in a new story, never missing a single issue — a remarkable achievement.

War, Dan left home to help King and country. Using his enormous strength and toughness (and often by accident) Dan sank U-boats and downed enemy planes, though his greatest wartime achievement was to keep the morale of Britain's children high during those dark times. During the war, paper was scarce and The Dandy appeared only once a fortnight but Dan continued to do his bit for the war effort by

Dudley D. Watkins (the D stood for Dexter) was born in Manchester in 1907, but the family moved to Nottingham when Dudley was a baby. Dudley's talent was spotted early and, at the tender age of ten, his painting of a local pageant was being exhibited at Nottingham Castle. The local newspaper, The Nottingham Guardian, acclaimed Dudley as a "schoolboy genius".

Continued overleaf.

5

Continued from previous page.

Watkins' first published cartoons appeared in 1923 in the Beacon, the staff magazine of the Boots Pure Drug company, where Dudley had taken a temporary job before becoming a full-time student at the Glasgow School of Art. While there, Dudley was recommended by the principal, Mr Else, to a representative of the publisher D. C. Thomson, who offered Dudley a six-month trial period with the firm. Six months became 44 years.

The first work Dudley undertook at his new job was to illustrate adventure stories in boys' papers and he was soon drawing the front cover of The Rover. Though he had done some comic work for The Rover Midget Comic in 1933, Dudley was considered an adventure story artist rather than a comic artist, but in 1936 Dudley's comic talents were brought to the fore when he began drawing The Broons and Oor Wullie for The Sunday Post Fun Section. It was the unqualified success of these pages which led Albert Barnes to offer Dudley the Desperate Dan page. Over the next thirty years Dudley would draw a succession of stories for The Dandy including Smarty Grandpa, Danny Longlegs and the wonderfully weird Our Teacher's A Walrus. He would contribute numerous pages to many comics: Lord Snooty, Tom Thumb, Jimmy And His Magic Patch and The Shipwrecked Circus among his many for The Beano; Ginger for The Beezer; Peter Piper for The Magic and a number of adaptations of classic novels for The Topper, including King Solomon's Mines, Kidnapped, Treasure Island and The Three Musketeers.

Dudley managed this extraordinary output despite producing a page each of Desperate Dan, Oor Wullie and The Broons every week. Perhaps most remarkable is that no matter how great the quantity of Dudley's output became, the quality of the artwork never wavered.

After Dudley's death, Dan continued to appear in The Dandy through reprints of Dudley's earlier pages, allowing a whole new generation of children to see these stories for the first time. Now Desperate Dan stories appeared in annuals and summer specials drawn by Charles Grigg, but it wasn't

Some of Dudley Watkins' many other characters. Mickey the Monkey, Ginger and Lord Snooty.

until 1983 that new Dan strips were to appear in the weekly comic, this time drawn by Ken Harrison. For the first time Dan was in full colour, and what's more he was given two pages. The next year, after 47 years, Desperate Dan replaced Korky on the front cover of The Dandy and now ran to three pages, which is still the case at the time of going to press.

Now that we've gone over the background, let's head on out to Cactusville and Dan's very first story. The legend begins . . .

**Printed and Published in Great Briatin by D. C. THOMSON & CO., LTD.,
185 Fleet Street, London, EC4A 2HS.** © D. C. THOMSON & CO., LTD., 1997.
ISBN 0 85116 6571

See Our Danny In A Rage —
Wipe His Shack Right Off This Page.

The Dandy December 11th, 1937.

Desperate Danny Is The Limit —
Eats His Hash With Poison In It.

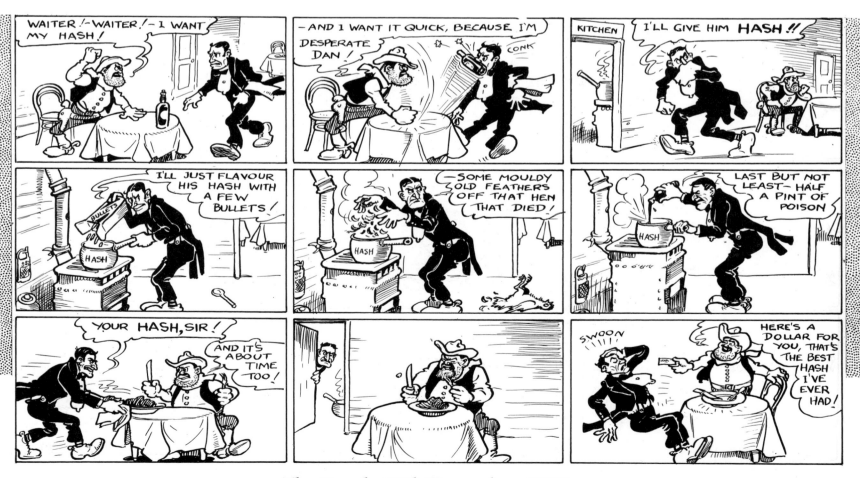

The Dandy 18th December, 1937.

Hear All The Boatmen Start To Wail —
When Dan Makes Himself A Gale

The Dandy March 5th, 1938.

Desperate Dan Has Got The Hiccup —
And Some Trouble He Sure Does Kick Up!

The Dandy April 23rd, 1938.

Desperate Dan Just Puffs And Blows —
And Out The Roaring Fire Goes.

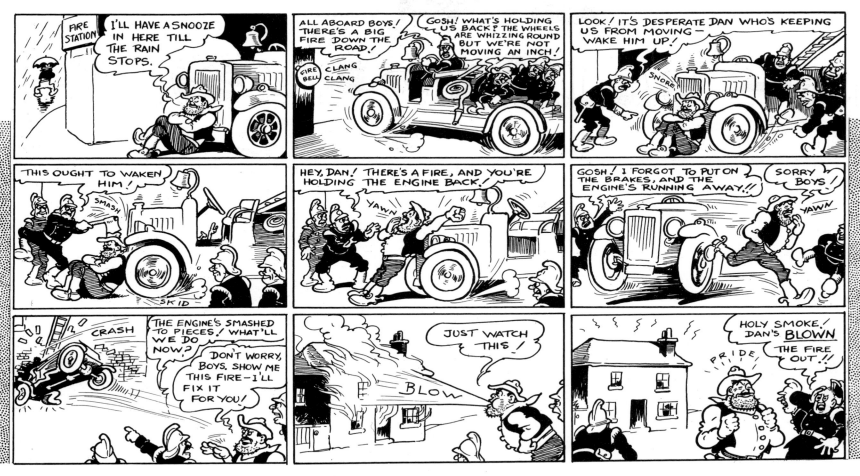

The Dandy April 30th, 1938.

Dan's Lost The Boat — He Takes A Jump —
Lands Through The Bottom With A Thump!

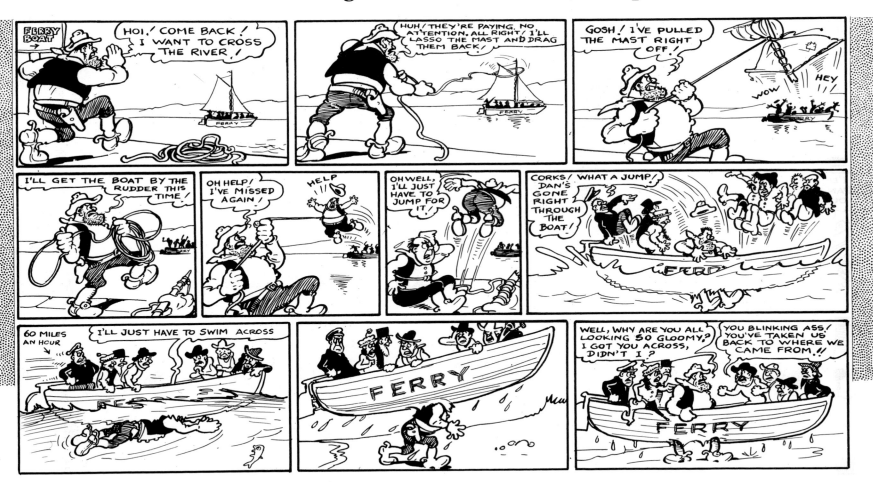

The Dandy August 20th, 1938.

You've Just Got To Raise Your Hat To — Rough, Tough Danny's Home-Made Statue!

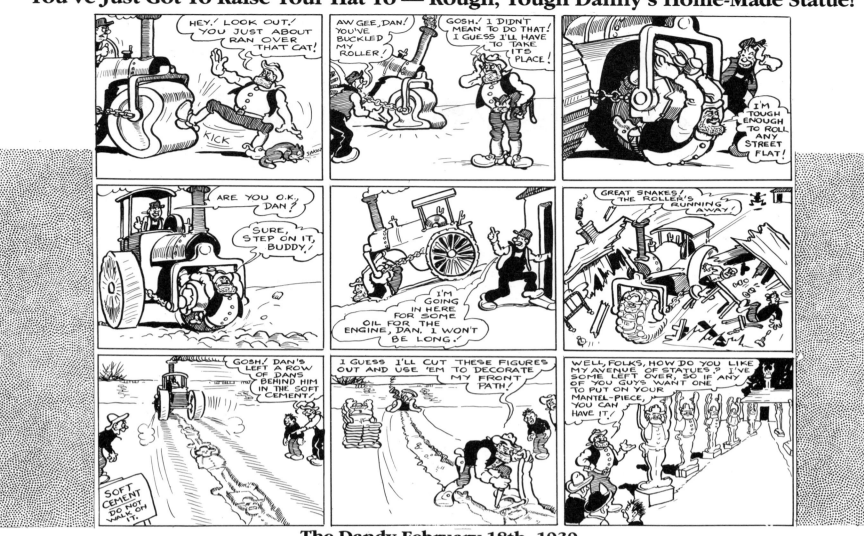

The Dandy February 18th, 1939.

If You Value Your Health At All — You'll Keep Clear When Dan Kicks A Ball.

The Dandy March 18th, 1939.

Robin Hood Was A Stout Bowman — He Didn't Have Nothin' On Desperate Dan.

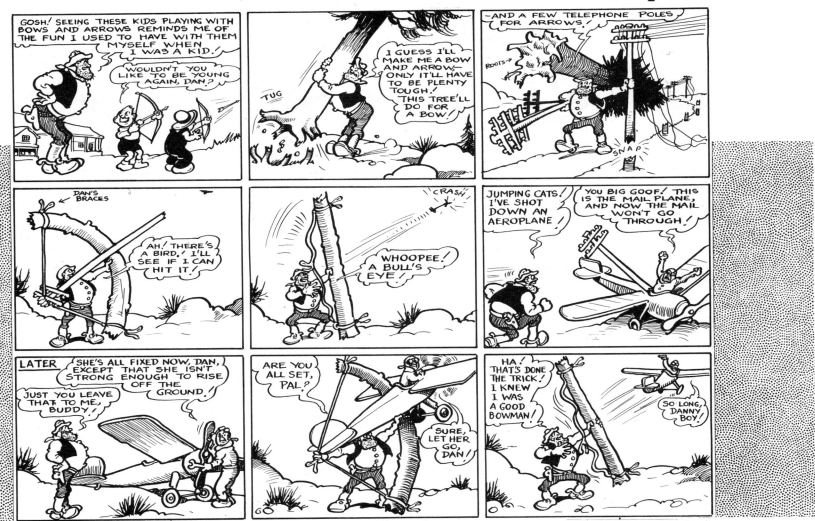

The Dandy April 15th, 1939.

"Oh Boy! Oh Boy!" The Kids All Yell — "Dan's Swimming Bath Is Simply Swell!"

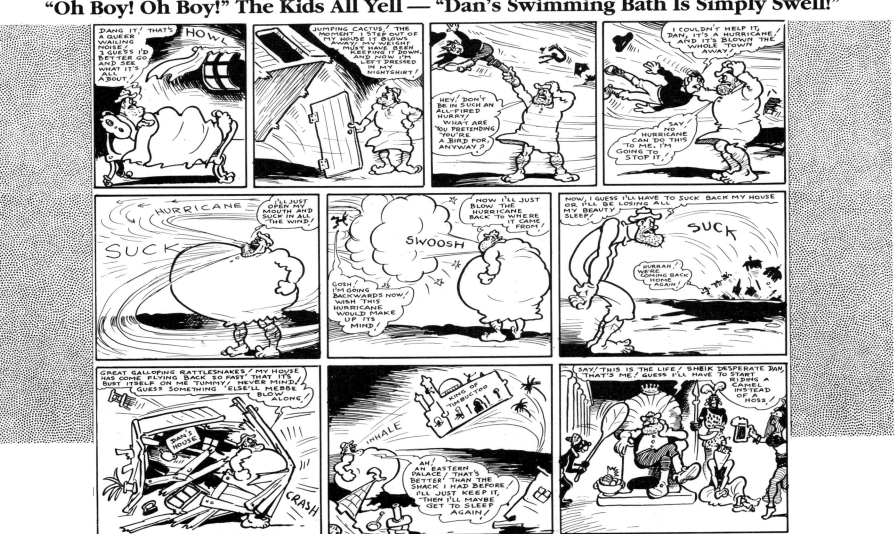

The Dandy April 22nd, 1939.

London's Wrecked! Gee, What A Sight — Dan Called There On His World Flight!

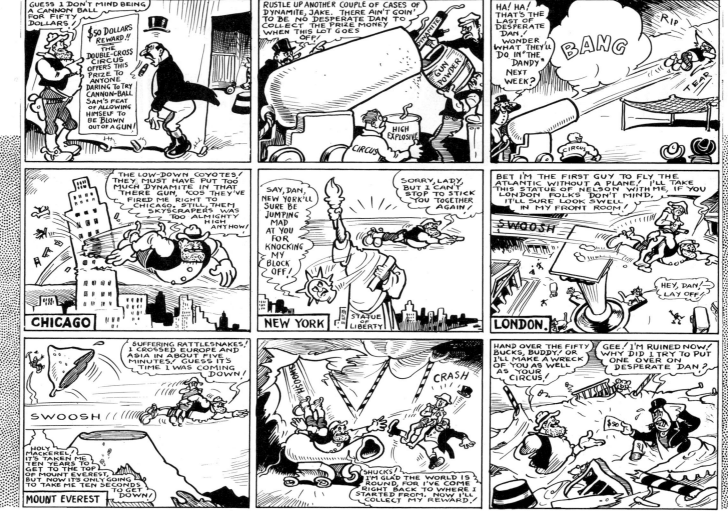

The Dandy August 19th, 1939.

Watch Danny Blow With Might And Main — His Breath Is Like A Hurricane!

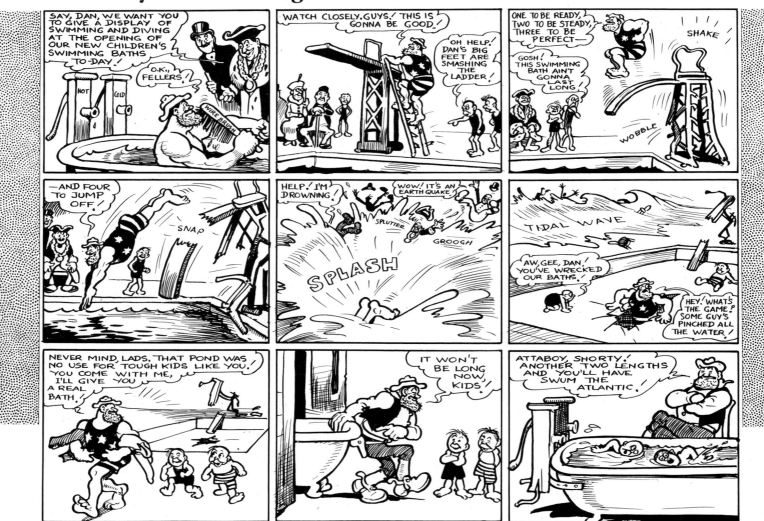

The Dandy September 23rd, 1939.

'Cos Danny's Wanting To Grow Slim —
Two Tanks Play Tug o'War With Him.

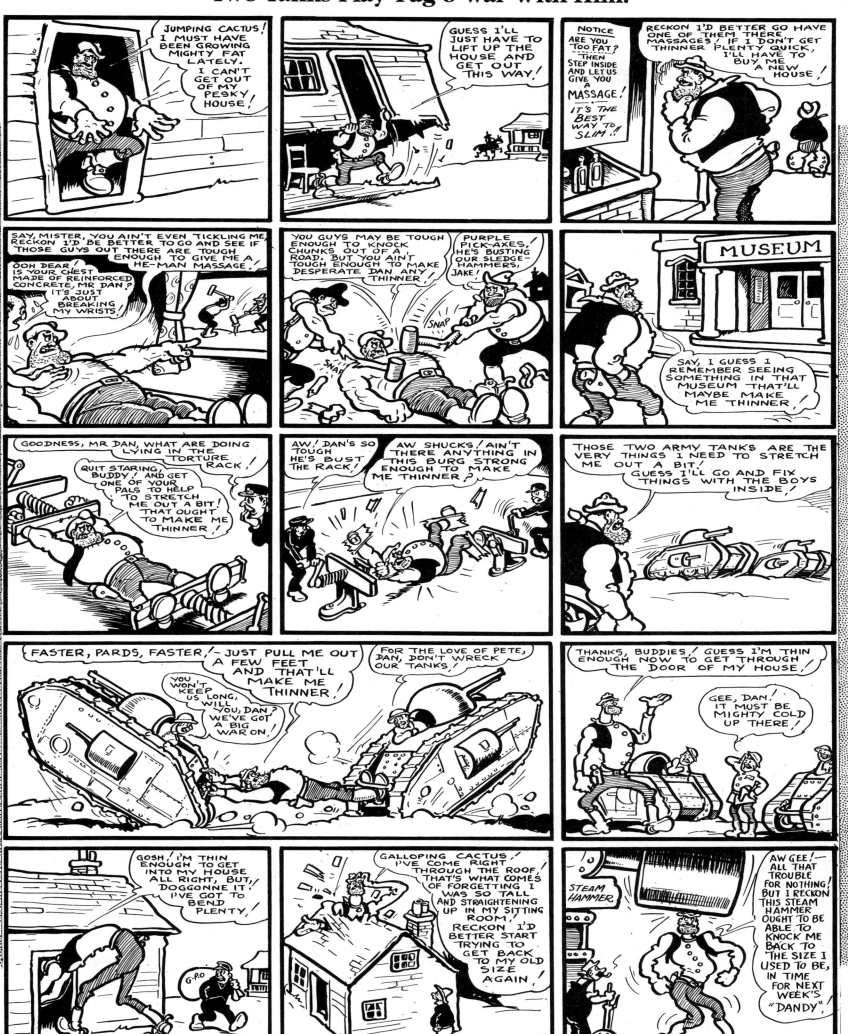

The Dandy February 3rd, 1940.

Dan Poultices A Great Big Bump —
Puts Molten Lead Upon The Lump.

People Gape And Bellow "Look-Ah!" — At Desperate Danny's Giant Hookah.

The Dandy September 28th, 1940.

Look At Desperate Dan, Coo Lumme —
A Bomb Is Bouncing Off His Tummy.

Dan's Trying To Get A Dazzling Smile —
His Toothbrush Is A Great Big File.

Dan Shouts "Sweep"! There's Such A Din —
That He Blows All The Windows In.

FOLLOWING the instant success of The Dandy Comic, the obvious next step was a larger, hard-backed Dandy Annual, to be published just in time to be the ideal Christmas present.
The first annual, The Dandy Monster Comic 1939, went on sale in Autumn 1938 and was as big a hit as the weekly comic had been. Autumn 1939 saw The Dandy Monster Comic 1940 published, and another followed each year until 1953, when the title was changed to simply, The Dandy Book, which remains the title today. Christmas and The Dandy annual have become linked. For generations of children, Christmas just wouldn't be Christmas without the Dandy Book.
Only two characters have appeared in every annual — Korky the Cat and Desperate Dan. The extra space afforded by the annual format was especially suited to showing Desperate Dan's muscular escapades, resulting in larger and more memorable illustrations than were possible in the weekly.
Dan proved such a success in the annuals that there have been five Desperate Dan Books, appearing in 1954, 1979, 1991, 1992 and 1993, each dedicated solely to Cactusville's favourite son.

Dan Will Give You All A Laugh When He Goes And Joins The Raff.

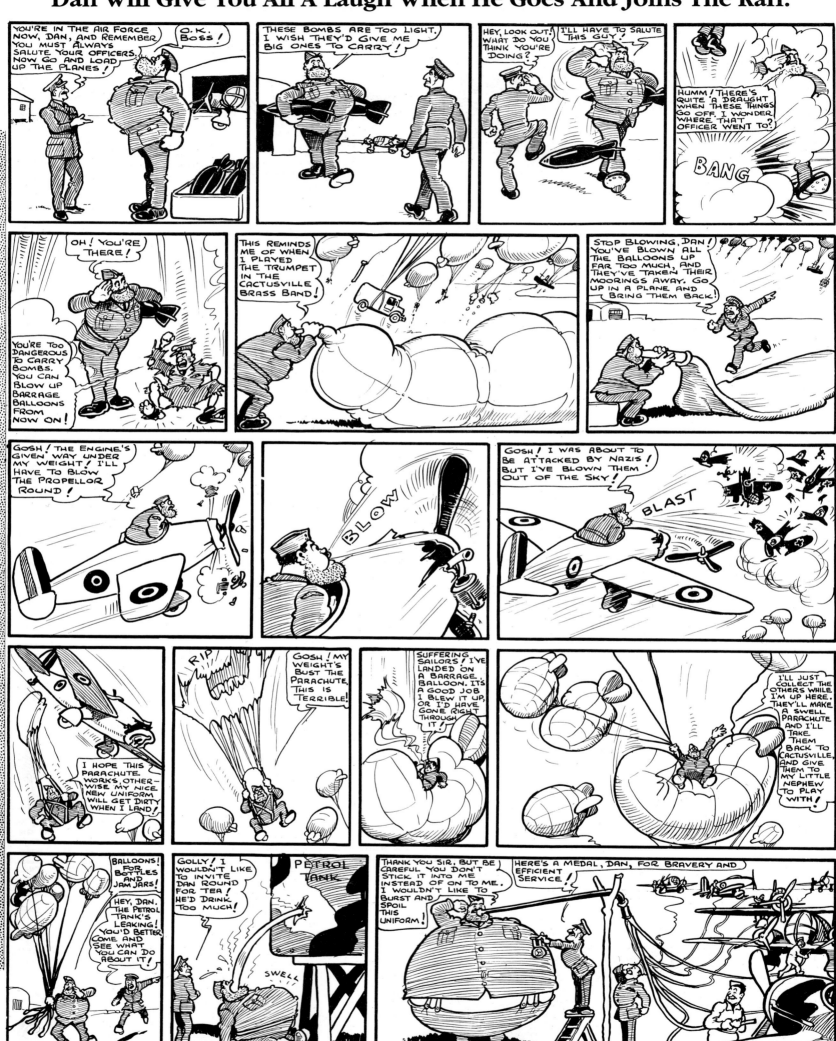

There's A Laugh Here For You All —
When Dan Becomes A Cannon-Ball.

As A Baker Dan Doesn't Shine —
Brick-Making Is More His Line.

As School Janitor Dan's A Disgrace —
See How Quickly He Wrecks The Place.

The Dandy September 30th, 1944.

Wow! Just Look How Danny's Pup Gives A Lion A Showing-Up.

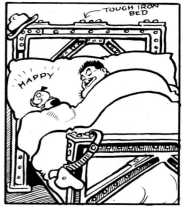

Dan Glides Over The Snow With Ease —
He Uses Trees In Place Of Skis.

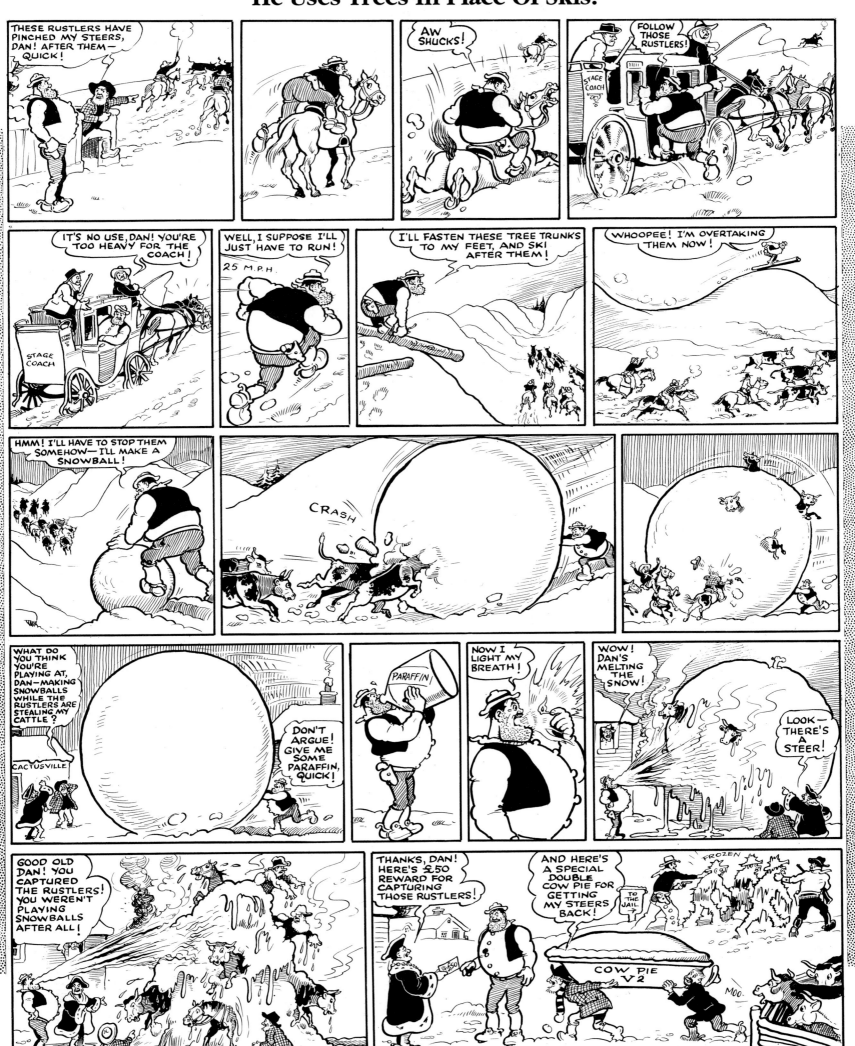

The Dandy December 9th, 1944.

Even Dan Is Not So Tough As His Own Monster Xmas Duff.

Plug In Nose, Bulb In Ear —
All But Dan Think The Black-Out Queer.

The Dandy March 31st, 1945.

There Isn't A Tougher Man Than Danny —
Nor A Tougher Woman Than His Old Granny.

Dan Has A Heart As Big As A Cart — He Is Kind To The Mouse He Found In His House.

The Dandy February 16th, 1946

Dan Has More Manners Than Tanners —
He's Very Polite, And Yet — Not Quite.

DESPERATE DAN

We first hear of Aunt Aggie when Dan attempts to write her a letter on 10.7.39.

A notable first — Desperate Dan dates his birthday as 11th March. This is in The Dandy dated 11.3.39.

In The Dandy dated 16.12.39 a double first. The first sight of Aunt Aggie and the first ever mention of cow-pie, Dan's favourite food for many years to come.

The first mention of Dan's home town Cactusville was on a bus, sinking in a flood of Dan's tears on 27.4.40.

Cactusville town centre, portrayed in The Dandy 2.8.41.

Dan's favourite nephew, Danny was first seen in 27.10.45. Danny went on to share many adventures with his famous uncle.

Dan Wrecks The Sail But Sails The Wreck —
Then Catches A Whale By The Scruff Of The Neck.

The Dandy June 22nd, 1946.

32

When Dan Goes Chimney-Sweeping It Is A Dirty Day —
But With Broomsticks And Rolling Pins, The Ladies Make Him Pay.

The Dandy September 28th, 1946.

Dan Makes A Face That's Such A Sight —
It Gives A Polar Bear A Fright.

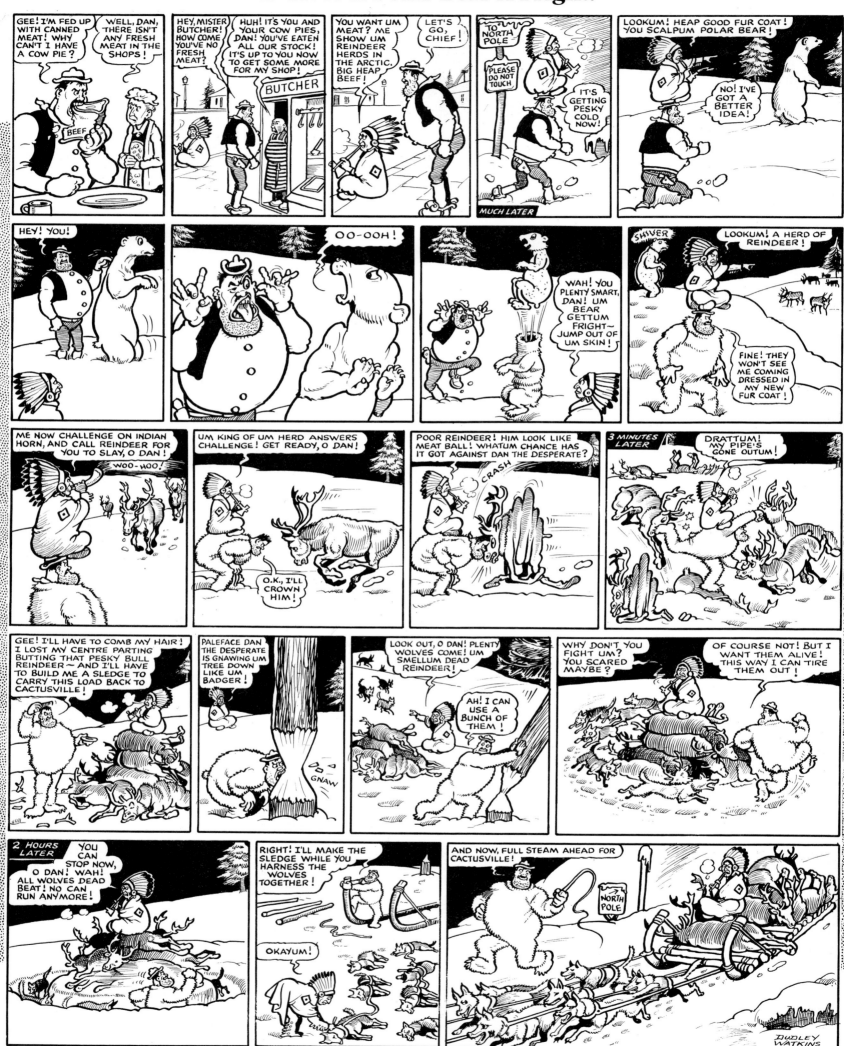

Angry Women Yell And Roar —
When Dan Brings Wolves To The Butcher's Door.

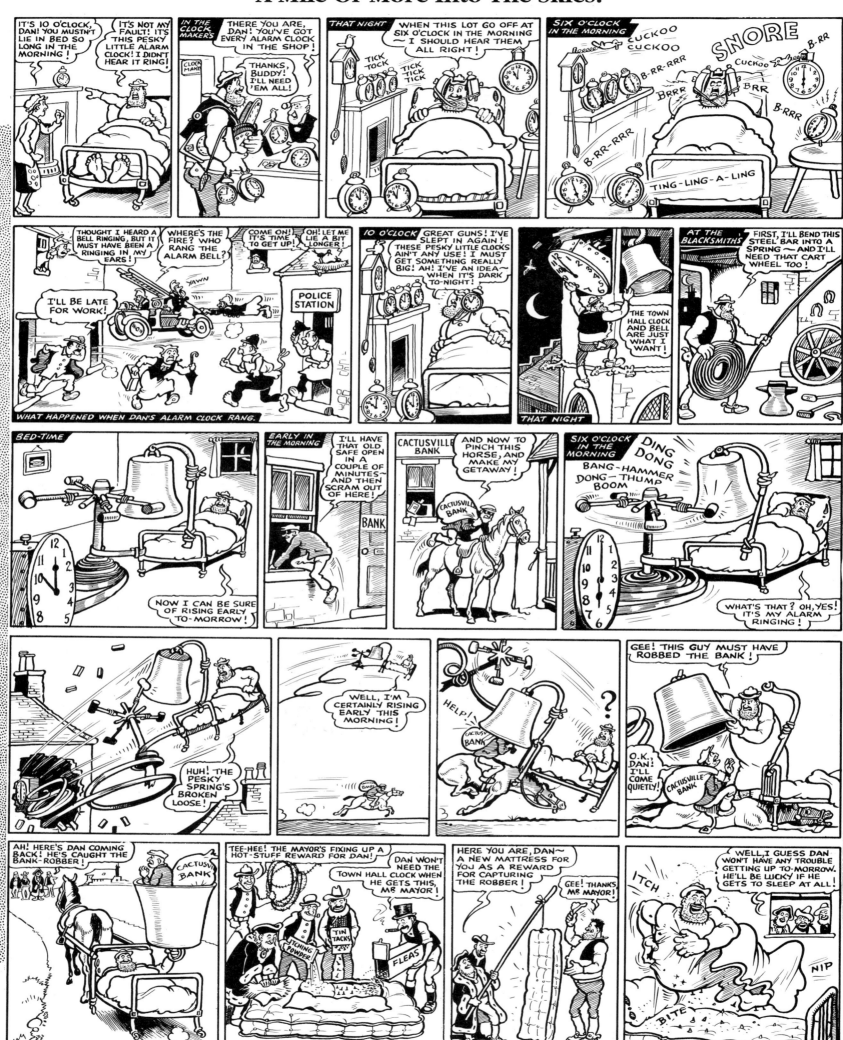

When Dan Sneezes Like A Hurricane —
A 'Painless' Dentist Feels The Pain.

The Dandy May 24th, 1947.

A Queer New Pal For Desperate Dan —
He's Jonah Jinx, The Bad Luck Man.

The Dandy February 26th, 1949.

Jonah Gets His Fortune Told, And He Is Warned "Beware — Of A Man With Long Short Legs, Who's Bald With Curly Hair."

Uncle Dan Gives Nephew Danny An April Fool Surprise —
And Danny Finds Some Meat Real FRESH In A Pie That Is Outsize.

A Face That Would Stop A Clock —
And A Body That Starts A Traffic Block.

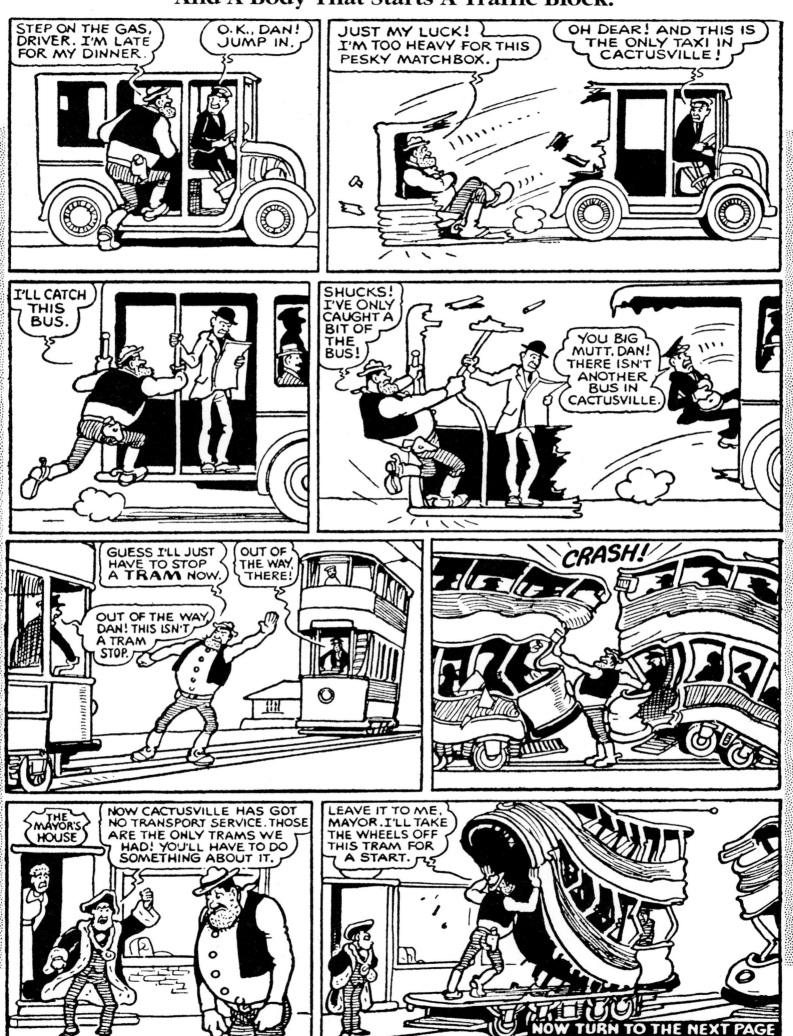

44

Out In The Garden Dan's Pipe Smoke —
Makes Even The Vegetables Choke.

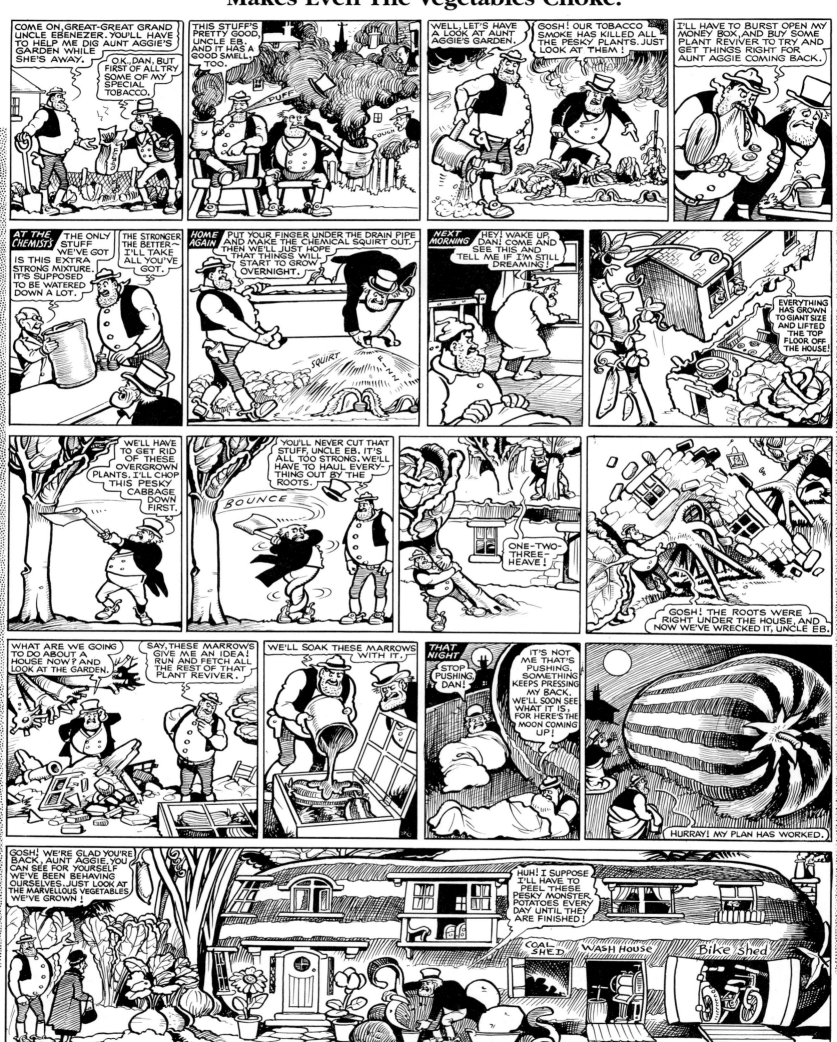

The Dandy June 17th, 1950.

Dan's Instrument Of Music Is Really Quite A Spanker —
His Doh, Ray, Me's Are Loud And Clear, Played On A Big Ship's Anchor.

Long before he became the star of the Dandy weekly comic's front cover, Desperate Dan had graced the back covers of Dandy annuals.

The
Dandy
Book
1954

The
Dandy
Book
1955

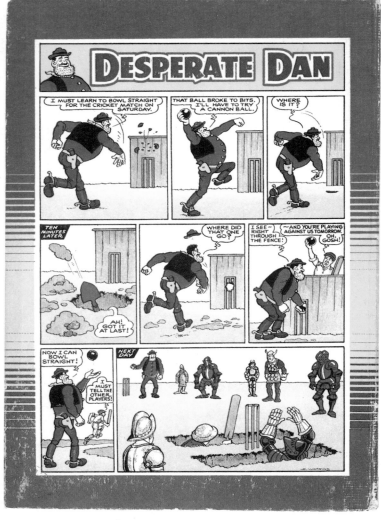

The
Dandy
Book
1956

The
Dandy
Book
1957

Dan appeared in a strip on the back of each Dandy book from 1954 till 1965, some of which are reproduced here.

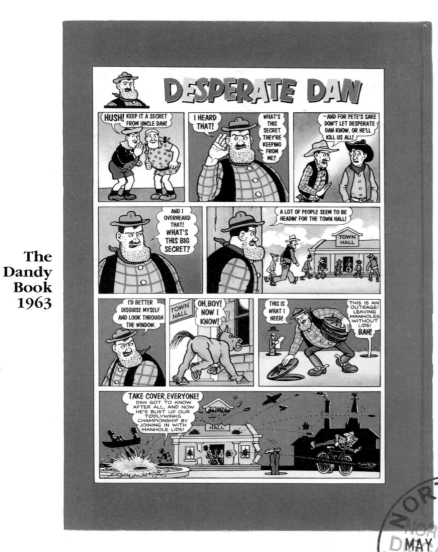

The Dandy Book 1963

The Dandy Book 1964

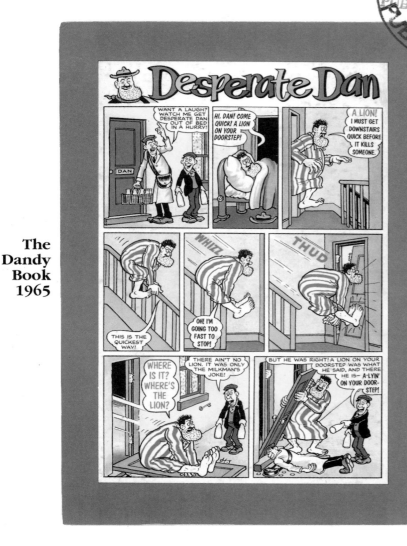

The Dandy Book 1965

The Dandy Book 1966

Dan's Such A Poor Magician You Just Could Not Believe —
He Gets Through Such A Tricky Act With Nothing Up His Sleeve.

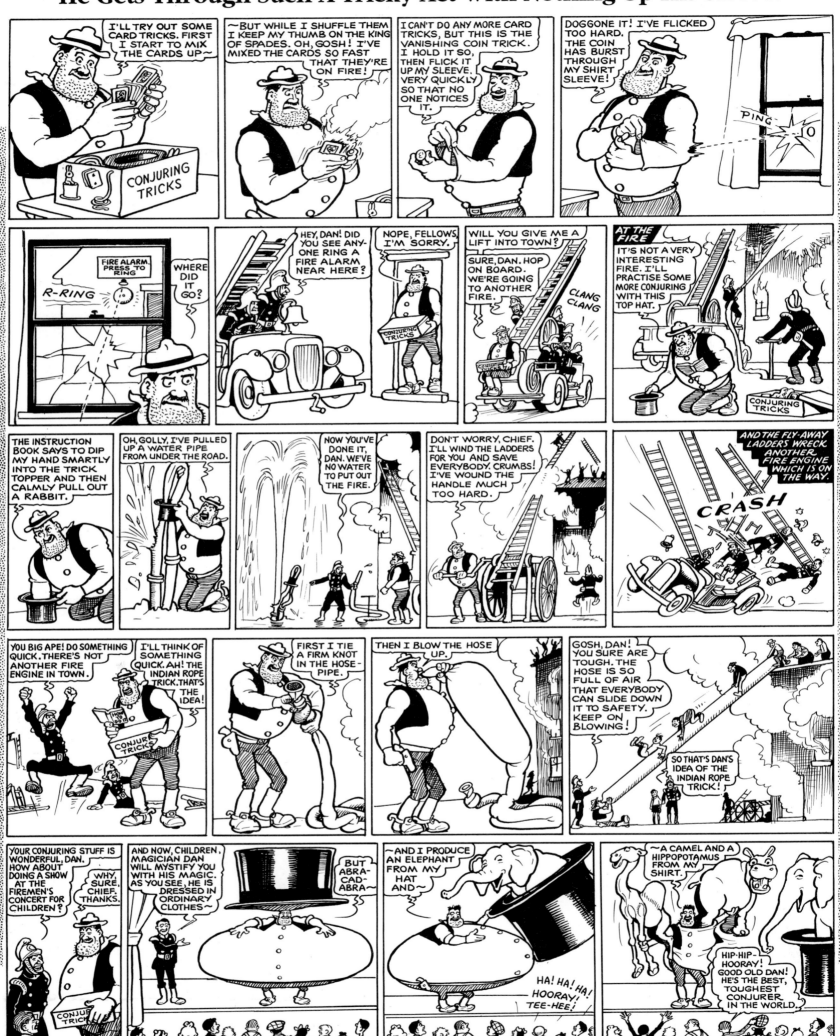

The Drums Go Bang, The Cymbals Clang, The Trumpet Blares Away —
And To Rid Themselves Of This One-Man Band, The People Gladly Pay!

The Dandy February 16th, 1952.

TWO DESPERATE TIDDLEY-WINKERS

Fun and Games

IN the sitting-room of the little house in Cactusville, where he lived with his Aunt Aggie, Desperate Dan was playing a quiet game of dominoes with his young nephew, Danny.

Dan was wearing his usual cowboy outfit, but young Danny was dressed in an Eton suit, with a stiff collar and a straw sailor hat. If it hadn't been for his muscles almost bursting through his clothes, young Danny would have looked a bit of a sissy. He was, in fact, very tough indeed.

"Shucks, Danny," groaned Desperate Dan. "You've nearly got me!"

He raised a massive fist and knocked on the table, to show he was missing a turn; but as his fist met the table-top there was a splintering crash.

"Gee! I've put my fist through the table!" cried Desperate Dan.

"That's ruined my table, too!" shrieked Aunt Aggie, who came in at that moment and spotted the damage.

"Why can't you play a nice quiet game like tiddley-winks?"

"OK, Aunt Aggie," said Dan peacefully. "We'll play tiddley-winks."

"But we haven't got any doggoned tiddley-winks, Uncle Dan," said Danny, after Aunt Aggie had left the room.

"Well, let's use these plates," replied Desperate Dan. "They're a bit big, but never mind. We'll use that big flower bowl as a catcher."

So they started playing tiddley-winks, and soon the air was filled with flying saucers and big plates.

When the Mayor fainted, Dan was quick to revive him!

"Ouch! Mind where you're firing, Danny," said Desperate Dan. "That plate caught me smack in the eye! Gee! That one went straight through the window. Look out! Oh, it's all right, my shot has missed you — but it's broken a mirror."

With plates flying everywhere, there was soon plenty of broken crockery lying about!

"This sure is a fine game, Uncle Dan," said Danny. "Oh dear! Now I've smashed the clock. But this one is going straight in the flower-bowl. Got it! But it's smashed the flower-bowl!"

While the fun was fast and furious, Aunt Aggie came on the scene again, and she nearly had a fit at the damage caused by the tiddley-wink players.

"Get out of here!" she yelled, reaching for her broom. "You and your pesky games! Go and play outside."

Aunt Aggie picked up the remaining unbroken plates and hurled them at Dan and his nephew, who lost no time in scooting out of doors.

"Come on, Danny," said Dan. "I guess we can have a game out here. We'll use this dustbin as a catcher and some manhole covers as 'men'. And take it easy. We don't want any more damage."

"Gee, Uncle Dan, these manhole covers sure fly through the air!" cried Danny, when the game was well under way. "Watch them go!"

The new tiddley-winks certainly did travel. One sliced through a car. Another cut the chimneys off a house after slicing the heads off three tailor's dummies in a wagon, and Danny sent off one that cut a man's hat, then halved a row of lamp-posts and a pillar-box.

"Shucks!" said Dan. "Oops! Sorry, Mr Mayor. I didn't see you coming along."

Dan's flying manhole cover had caught the Mayor of Cactusville plumb in the bread-basket just as he was coming round a corner.

Luckily for him it wasn't travelling edgewise, or he would have been sliced in half, too. But he folded up with a groan when the hefty iron disc hit him.

"Gosh, the Mayor's knocked out," said Desperate Dan. "What can we do?" Just at that moment the

Dan and his nephew needed ladders so that they could play snakes-and-ladders. They soon collected a few.

Cactusville water cart came trundling down the street.

"Water!" said Dan. "That's what he needs."

He picked up the water cart, bringing a frightened neigh from the horse as it was tossed high in the air. But Dan paid no attention to the horse. He up-ended the cart over the Mayor.

With half a ton of water doused all over him, the Mayor soon recovered consciousness, and he bounded to his feet with a howl of rage.

"Look at the damage you pesky tiddley-winkers are doing!" he roared. "Sufferin' polecats, there ain't a whole lamp-post left in town. Drat it! Why don't you play some harmless game? Look, over there some old men are playing draughts without causing damage."

He showed them a big outdoor draughts board.

"Now try playing draughts, or snakes-and-ladders, or something," he said as he hobbled off.

Great Snakes!

"SNAKES-and-ladders," said Dan thoughtfully. "I guess I'll have to think about this."

Desperate Dan and Nephew Danny wandered through Cactusville pondering on how they could have a quiet game somewhere. Dominoes and tiddley-winks had both resulted in damage, and the big draughts board was being used by the old men.

"Say, I got a dandy idea," exclaimed Desperate Dan. "We'll make an outdoor game of snakes-and-ladders and present it to the town! And we'll make it right here in the City Square. Look, it's all nicely marked out in squares."

"But, Uncle Dan, we need ladders and snakes and dice and a shaker, and we ain't got any of 'em," protested Danny.

"We will get them," said Dan, smiling happily. "Ladders first. Now, where can we get some pesky ladders? There's one over there by that half-painted house. I'll just collect it. Oops! Sorry, buddy; I didn't see you painting at the top of that ladder."

Dan had made a slight mistake by collecting a ladder on which the painter still perched, but he soon gave him the brush-off.

Danny found a nice big ladder. It was a pity it was attached to a factory chimney, but the strong boy got it free with a strong pull, though the chimney did fall down afterwards. Two steeple-jacks fell with it, but Danny caught them as they fell and put them on their feet.

"Look what I've got," beamed Dan, showing an armful of red-painted ladders. "I snatched them off a fire-engine going past."

"Oh, well, maybe it wasn't going to a fire anyway," said Danny.

"We'll soon have our game of snakes-and-ladders," said Dan. "We've got plenty of ladders now. We'll mosey along to the Zoo and borrow some snakes."

At Cactusville Zoo Dan found that the snake-keepers were only too willing to lend him their charges.

"Goody-goody!" said the head snake-keeper. "Now we can have a day's holiday! How are you going to carry all

A statue's pedestal for a dice and a church bell for a pitcher. Now Dan and Danny were all set to play games.

these snakes, Mr Dan?"

"Shucks! It's easy," grinned Dan. "Me and my young nephew here will roll 'em into a big ball just like Aunt Aggie rolls up her knitting wool."

"You hold and I'll wind, Uncle," said Danny.

Pythons, cobras, rattlesnakes, vipers and all sorts of other snakes were powerless in the beefy hands of Desperate Dan, and he held them out while Danny wound them round one another.

"Now back to the City Square," said Dan. "But we still want a dice and a shaker."

When they got to the City Square they found both those things fairly handy.

"I'll just pinch the pedestal from under this statue," said

cold shoulder. They don't deserve to have good citizens like us."

Dan didn't realise it, but quite a few of the citizens of Cactusville had looked in at the City Square, but the sight of the poisonous snakes, writhing and hissing in their steel hoops, caused them to leave the Square quicker than they came.

"I wonder where everybody is?" murmured Desperate Dan, as he leaned against one of the pillars of the City Hall. "Gee! What's that rumbling noise? Shucks! This pillar is collapsing. What a nuisance! And now the front of the building is falling down. But what's this? Gee! It's the Mayor and all his Council falling out of the upstairs windows. They must have been watching us after all,

It was a desperate game of snakes-and-ladders. The snakes were alive!

Dan. "It's nice and square and should make a dandy dice when I put the spots on it."

"OK," said Danny. "And I'll shin up to the church tower and borrow the bell for a shaker."

"Shucks," said Dan, as he whisked away the square pedestal of the big statue. "I seem to have broken the statue to bits, but the pedestal is still OK, and that's the main thing. Ah! Here comes Danny with the bell. What a pity he's bent the church tower in getting it."

"The pesky snakes won't stay still, Uncle Dan," said Danny. "They seem peeved."

"Shucks! We'll soon fix them. I'll borrow these croquet hoops from the park and peg the snakes down with them. Gee, Danny! Won't the Mayor be pleased that we've made this fine big snakes-and-ladders board for the town?"

Kneeling in the middle of Cactusville City Square, Desperate Dan and young Danny rolled their huge concrete dice in the church bell shaker and had a ding-dong game of snakes-and-ladders. But Dan began to look a little peeved as the minutes ticked by and the City Square remained deserted.

"Shucks! Nobody to watch us at all," he grumbled. "Not a single spectator in sight. It kinda looks as if people ain't interested. We've been to a lot of trouble to construct this game for Cactusville, and all we get is the

Danny."

"Welcome to the opening of Cactusville's first open-air snakes-and-ladders pitch," said Danny, shaking the Mayor's hand as he picked him up. "Are you going to have a game with us?"

The Mayor was so dazed that he couldn't reply.

"You throw first, Mr Mayor," beamed Dan. "Aw, I'm sorry. You've dropped the dice. It's too heavy for you? Never mind, I'll throw it for you. A six? Great! Oh, dear, you've got to go down that python. Off you go."

Still a bit dazed, the Mayor staggered on to the marked squares, but when he found the python's forked tongue flickering around his feet he bolted.

"Shucks!" said Dan. "The Mayor has run away. Still, you can be next, Mr Town Clerk. I'll throw the dice for you. Oh, dear! It's crashed right through the pavement into some sort of cellar. I wonder what's down there?"

Blow Cannonball

AS Desperate Dan peered into the cellar there was a loud whoosh! And a column of smoke poured out of the hole in the pavement.

"Gosh, Uncle Dan," said Danny. "That must have been the boiler room down there, and our big dice has smashed up the furnace and started a fire."

When Dan and Danny start to puff — Blow-cannonball is mighty rough!

"Gee, it looks as if you're right," said Dan, "Here come the fire engines."

"Hey, Dan," bellowed the Fire Chief, "what have you done with our ladders?"

"Oh, dear," said Dan, looking at his giant snakes-and-ladders game. "They're all here, but that pesky dice bouncing about all over them has broken every one."

"That's too bad," replied the Fire Chief. "There are a lot of people on the top floor of the City Hall, and we've got to get them down."

"Leave it to me, Chief," said Dan. "Give me a hand to collect these snakes, Danny."

Soon Dan and Danny had collected all the snakes from their game, and once again Desperate Dan tied the reptiles end to end.

"Now I'll just make them into a lasso like this," he said, making a running noose at the end of the long line of snakes.

Dan was a great hand with a lasso, even one made of snakes. His first throw roped the City Hall flagpole.

"Well, I guess if the townsfolk of Cactusville don't like my snakes-and-ladders they might like blow football," answered Dan.

"That's a great idea," said Danny. "We can mark goals on the walls."

Dan looked around the wreck of the City Square, and then his eyes lit up. Parked outside the remains of the City Hall was an ancient iron siege gun — and beside it a stack of big cast-iron balls.

"They'll do for footballs," said Dan. "We'll take a drainpipe each and get started, Danny."

"I'll have first blow," declared Danny, placing a hefty cannonball in front of his pipe. "Shucks! I've blown too hard."

Faster than it ever travelled in the days when it was fired from a gun, the cannonball whistled through the air.

"Gee, it's gone straight through the electric power station. Now it's your turn, Uncle Dan. Shucks! You're no better; your shot has broken a telegraph pole and taken the roof off the school!"

Blow-football wasn't a parlour game the way Dan and Danny played it — with drain-pipes and cannon-balls!

Seizing hold of his queer life-line, Dan swarmed up to the roof of the burning building.

Climbing down inside the City Hall, Desperate Dan soon found what he was looking for. It was the main staircase leading down to the ground floor.

"This is much better than a ladder," he grunted. He got hold of the banisters and heaved. Up came the staircase. But the windows weren't wide enough for it to go through. So Dan had to widen them.

With his bare hands he pushed away a large part of the wall, and then he lowered his uprooted staircase out through the gap and down to the ground.

"Good old Dan!" cried the folk as they walked down the stairway on to the City Square.

"Gee! It looks as if I needn't have bothered," said Dan. "The fire brigade have put the fire out."

As he walked back to rejoin Danny, Dan noticed a big hole in the ground. He jumped down into it and yanked out two lengths of drain-pipe.

"What do you want those drain-pipes for, Uncle Dan?" asked Danny.

Dan and Danny kept trying to score goals with their cannonballs, but they kept missing and the shots went screaming all over Cactusville and doing all sorts of damage.

"Dan! Dan! You've got to stop at once," said the Mayor, who came running on to the scene.

"Aw gee, Mr Mayor," groaned Dan. "All we want is a nice quiet parlour game we can play."

"All right, all right," said the Mayor hastily. "How about ludo? In the power station yard there are lots of big wooden cable drums you can use as counters. And take 'em out on the prairie where you can't do any damage!"

"Ludo!" cried Desperate Dan and Danny together. "That sure sounds good."

So Desperate Dan collected his big concrete dice from the cellar of the City Hall, and with his snakes tucked under his arm to use in marking out the "board", he followed Danny out of the town. They trundled half a dozen big cable-drums each, and soon they had settled down on the prairie for an outside game of ludo.

The Cactusville folk breathed freely once more!

The Dandy April 5th, 1952.

56

If You're Needing Coal Delivered, Dan's The Man To Tell —
And Maybe, If You're Lucky, You'll Get A Horse As Well.

The Dandy April 19th, 1952.

Here's Something That Is Funny, If That's What You Like —
Big Dan Digs A Moat While He's Riding A Bike.

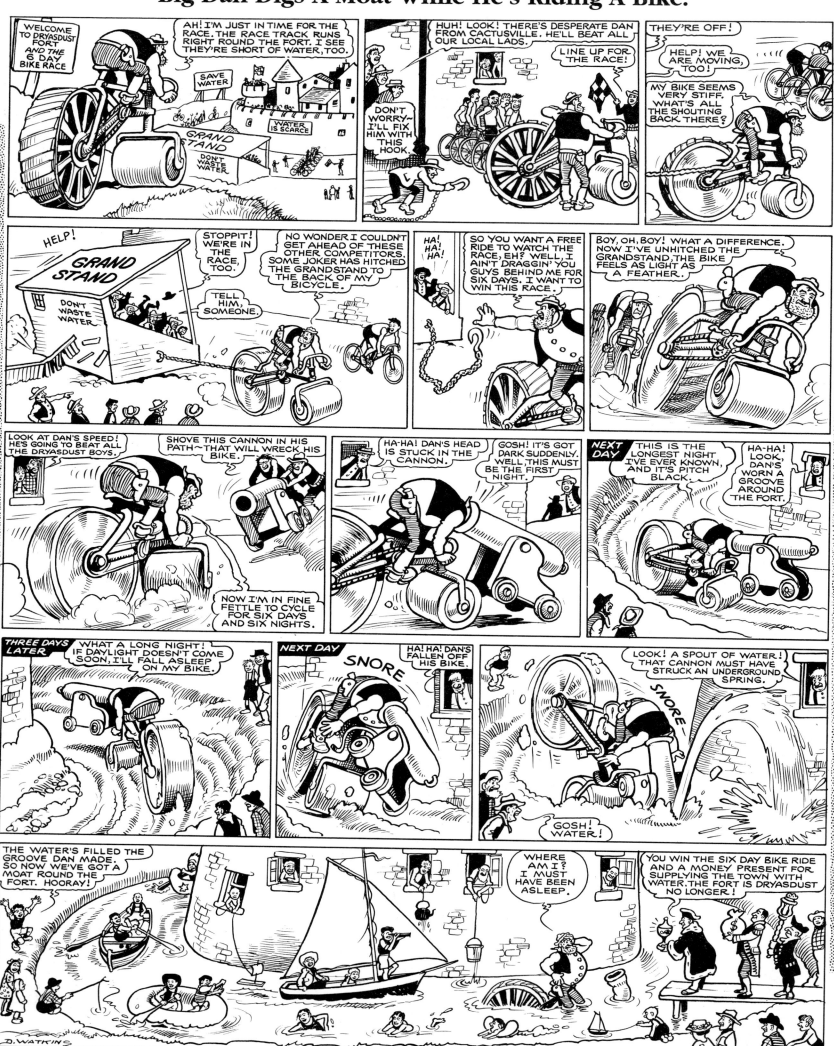

The Dandy August 9th, 1952.

A Wild Man Enters Dan's Barber Shop, And From There On —
He Fights Like A Tiger To Keep His Hair On.

Big Dan Is In London For The Very First Time — And That's Why Big Ben Has Ceased To Chime!

The Dandy June 6th, 1953.

The DESPERATE DAN Song

MY name is Desperate Dan, Desperate Dan.
I'm the world's toughest man, yes I am.
Come and test my frying-pan,
And eat bully in the can,
And you'll be as tough a man
As Desperate Dan.

I HAVE a giant's frame, giant's frame.
Bandits tremble at my name, and my fame.
Outlaw horses blush with shame,
Kick my chin and then go lame,
But for me it's just a game
To make them tame!

I'M as strong as any six, any six.
Grizzly bears I love to fix with my tricks.
I can break their bones like sticks,
Bend their backs like candle-wicks;
From my fists as hard as bricks
They get their licks.

WHERE I live in Cactusville, Cactusville,
I always eat my fill of cow-pie grill.
Old Aunt Aggie's python swill,
It is guaranteed to kill,
But you know I'm living still —
And never ill!

NOW it's time I slung my hook, slung my hook,
For I'm off to catch a crook and a spook.
Are they hiding by a brook?
Hiding in some shady nook?
Shucks! Just come and take a look
Inside my book.

DUDLEY D WATKINS

Dan Can Hear No Noise At All, And Thinks It's Very Rum —
It Seems The Desperate Man Is Deaf, And Some Say He Is Dumb.

Dan Likes To Be Polite, So His Face Turns Red —
When He Can't Lift His Hat Because It's Soldered To His Head.

The Dandy January 7th, 1956.

There Are Fighting Men In Texas, Forever Disturbing The Peace —
But They're Going To Be Very Quiet, After Dancing With Big Dan's Niece.

Dan's Three-Seater Bike Is In A Smash, And That's The Principal Cause — Of Making The Queerest Easter Egg That There Ever Was!

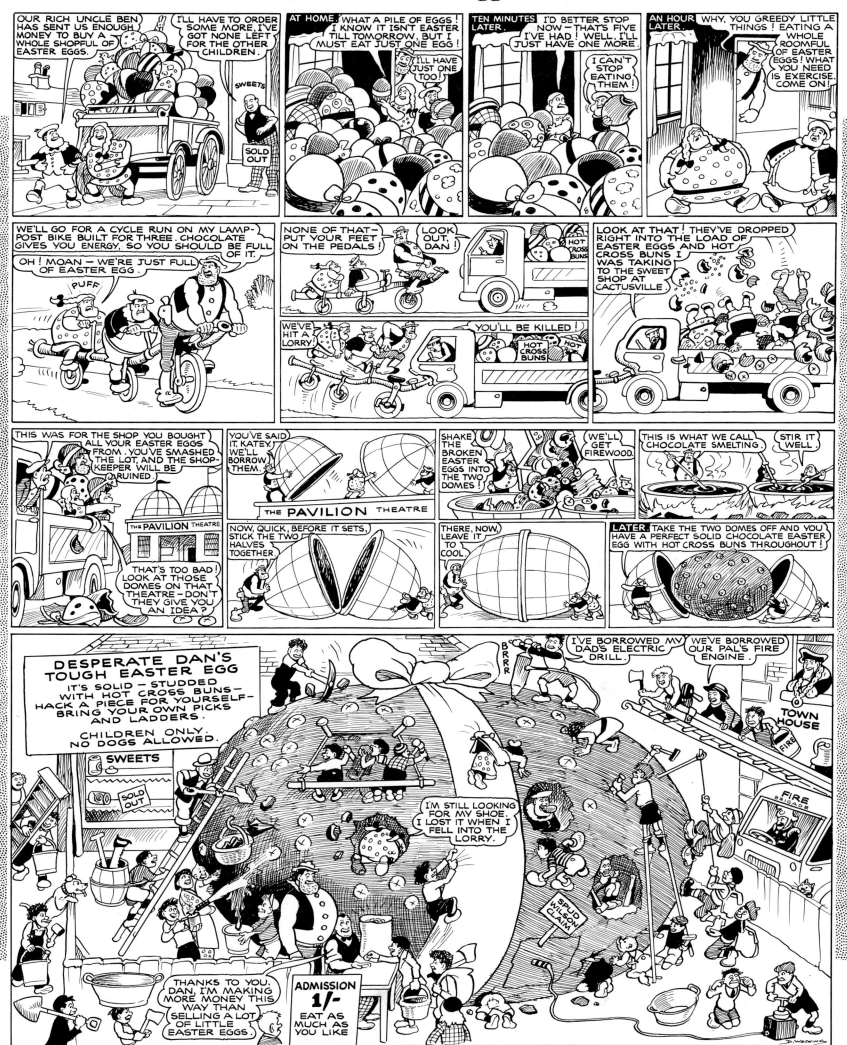

The Dandy April 20th, 1957.

Gold! Everybody Likes It —
But Only Dan Strikes it!

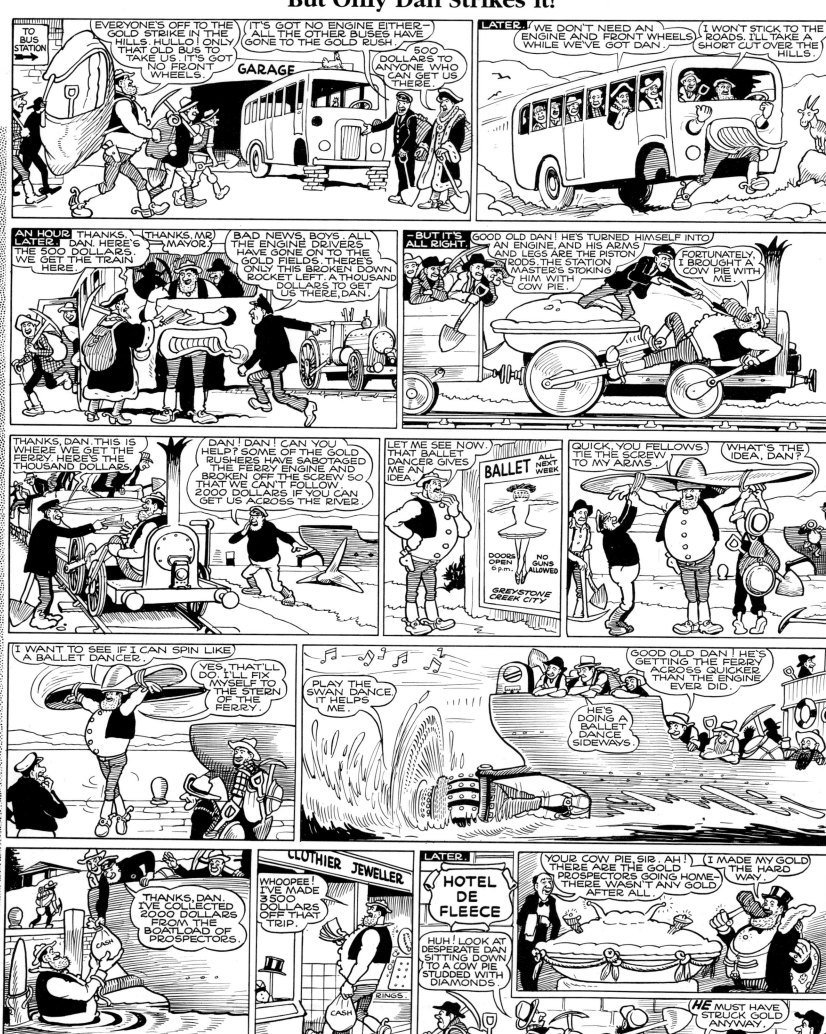

The Dandy May 31st, 1958.

Dan's A Very Hungry Man, With A Problem He Must Face —
How Can He Satisfy His Appetite With Gentlemanly Grace?

A Real White Christmas, Hip-Hip-Hooreigh —
And Desperate Dan Becomes A Sleigh!

The Dandy December 26th, 1959.

Desprit Jake In The Cave-Man Days —
Was Just Like Dan In His Desprit Ways.

Dandy Annual, 1960.

The Dandy May 21st, 1960.

Dan Is So Light He Thinks He's A Moth —
That's Why He Eats The Tablecloth!

The Dandy June 25th, 1960.

Five Crooks Think There Oughta Be A Ban On —
Desperate Dan, The Human Cannon!

The Dandy February 18th, 1961.

When You're On Holiday At The Seaside —
Dan's The Man Not To Be Beside!

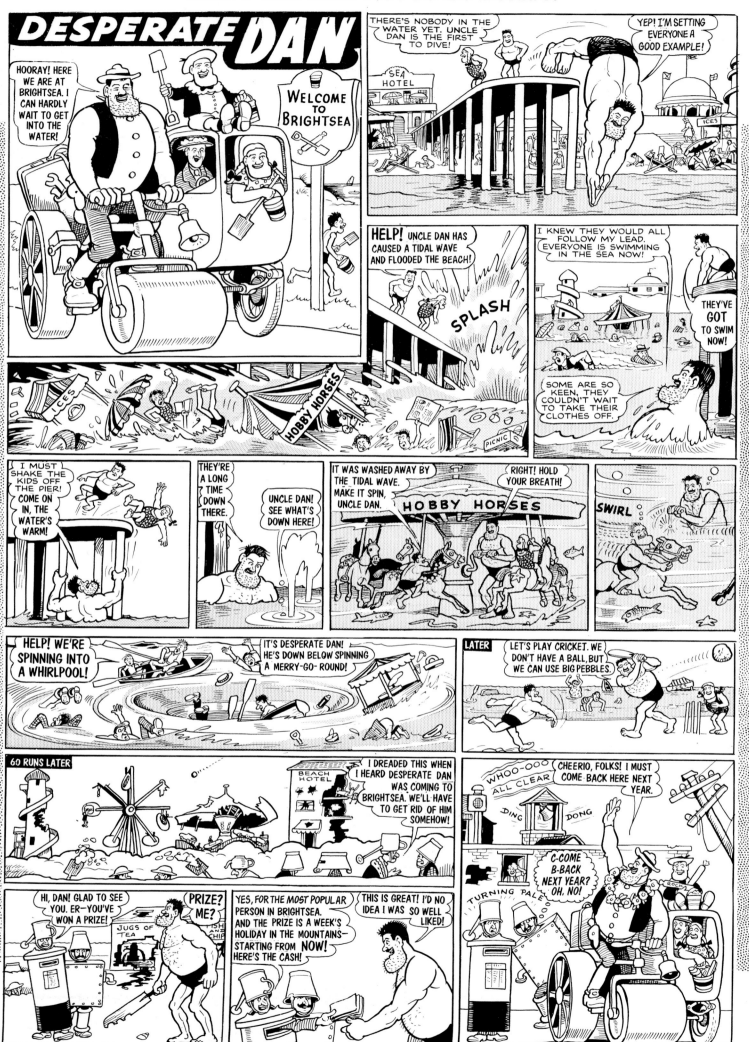

The Dandy June 24th, 1961.

Here's Where You Get A Great Big Laugh —
At Desperate Dan's School Photograph.

HO-HO-HO! UNCLE DAN'S SCHOOL PHOTO! HA-HA-HA!

I'LL TELL YOU HOW IT CAME TO BE TAKEN.

I was just a little fella at school.

DAN!

One day the Headmaster called me out and sent me home, telling me not to come back in the afternoon!

L FOR LAMB

B FOR BUNNY

Of course, I went tearing off—and though I saw teachers carrying out forms and nailing them in a tier like a grandstand, I paid no heed to that.

NAILS

I told my Ma I'd got a holiday—but she didn't believe it. She gave me my dinner—

—then she went to the neighbours to find if this holiday yarn was true.

When she came back she was foamin'—she dragged me to the pump and gave me a scrubbin'!

Then she put on my best suit—

—and on the way to school she told me the school photo was being taken that afternoon—and the Head had sent me home because he reckoned I'd crack the camera.

When we got there they were all in place on the built-up forms, and the camera guy was ready. Ma says, "Go on, son, get into that photo!"

SO I DID, AND THAT'S HOW IT TURNED OUT!

PHOTOGRAPH ALBUM

NOW TURN OVER AND SEE THE SCHOOL PICTURE FOR YOURSELF.

Dandy Annual, 1961.

Big Dan Bowls A Half-Ton Yorker —
In Revenge For Being Called A Porker!

The Dandy March 10th, 1962.

Ever Seen A Noisy Pillar Box? —
Here's One That Walks And Talks!

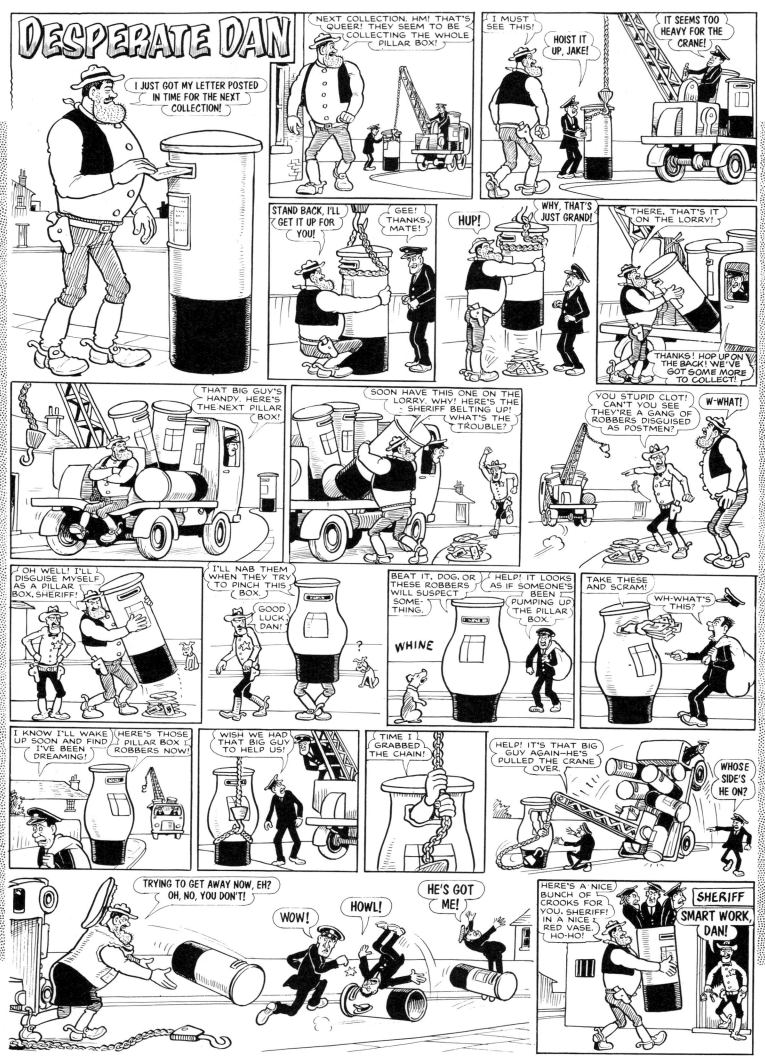

The Dandy October 10th, 1964.

A Cat Burglar Hid Beneath Dan's Bed — And Now He Has A Very Flat Head!

Why Did Dan Run Away From Home? —
He Really Had No Need To Roam!

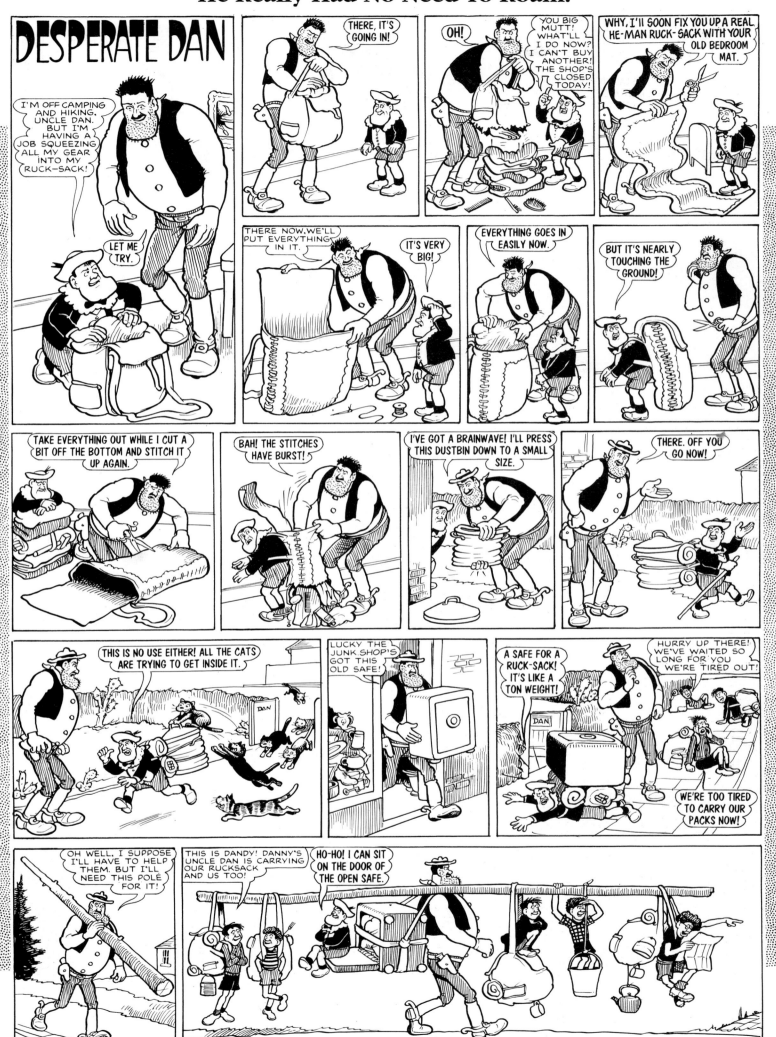

The Dandy September 11th, 1965.

Dan Is Bold, And A Perfect Batter — And Yet He's Bowled! What's The Matter?

The Dandy June 18th, 1966.

Dan's New Pal Is All The Rave —
It Has A Mouth That's Like A Cave!

DESPERATE DAN'S

WELL, LOOK WHAT I'VE FOUND—ONE OF MY OLD SCHOOL BOOKS! IT SURE BRINGS BACK SOME HAPPY MEMORIES....

I REMEMBER MY OLD SCHOOL DESK. THEY HAD TO SEND FOR A TANK DESIGNER TO BUILD ONE TOUGH ENOUGH FOR ME.

POOR OLD MISS PRIM BROKE SO MANY CANES TRYING TO WHACK ME THAT SHE MADE HER OWN SPECIAL ONE—WITH A CRICKET BAT AND A FRYING PAN! I JUST PRETENDED IT HURT ME.

OOH! OUCH!

WHACK WHACK

WHAT A LAUGH IT WAS WHEN OUR MUSIC TEACHER TRIED TO TEACH ME TO PLAY THE FRENCH HORN. I BLEW SO HARD I STRAIGHTENED IT OUT AND WINDED HIM!

POOF

WHAT A ROW I GOT FOR RUINING THE SCHOOL RAILINGS. ALL I DID WAS PLAY HEADERS AGAINST THEM—WITH A STONE BALL!

Schooldays

WRITING LINES NEVER BOTHERED ME. I JUST PILED A THOUSAND SHEETS OF PAPER ON THE FLOOR AND WROTE ON THE TOP ONE. I PRESSED SO HARD, THE WRITING WENT RIGHT THROUGH TO THE BOTTOM.

I REMEMBER BEIN' LATE FOR SCHOOL ONE DAY. I THOUGHT I COULD SNEAK IN A DIFFERENT WAY WITHOUT BEING SEEN, BUT I GUESS I MADE TOO MUCH NOISE.

YOU ARE LATE, DANIEL!

SORRY, MISS!

DANIEL! LET ME OUT THIS MINUTE!

IN OUR HANDIWORK CLASS THE OTHER KIDS USED TO MAKE BASKETS. I MADE SOMETHING MORE USEFUL — A CAGE FOR TEACHER, WOVEN OUT OF THE SCHOOL RAILINGS.

MISS PRIM ASKED ME TO WIPE THE BLACKBOARD ONCE — BUT ONLY ONCE! I RUBBED SO HARD, I WIPED IT WHITE!

$10 \times 8 \times 3 = 240$

I USED TO PLAY LEAPFROG IN THE PLAYGROUND. BUT MY PALS WEREN'T TOUGH ENOUGH TO STAND UP TO MY WEIGHT, SO I HAD TO BORROW STATUES FROM THE PARK. OH, BOY! WAS THE KEEPER MAD!

MY LOVELY STATUES!

MY SCHOOL SATCHEL WAS AN OUTSIZE ONE. IT HAD TO BE TO CARRY MY COW PIE LUNCH!

COW PIE

THE WRESTLERS

STRENGTH & BEAUTY

YEP! THEY SURE WERE HAPPY DAYS, FOLKS!

The 1980's saw big changes for Desperate Dan, with new strips drawn by Ken Harrison, and in 1984, Dan finally made it to the front cover, replacing Korky the Cat.

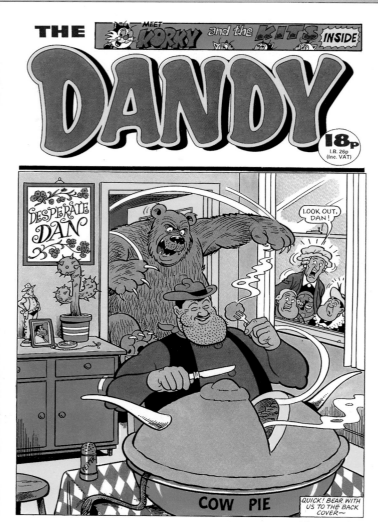

The Dandy September 19th, 1987.

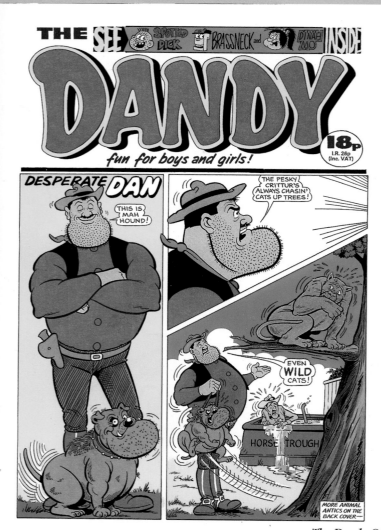

The Dandy October 3rd, 1987.

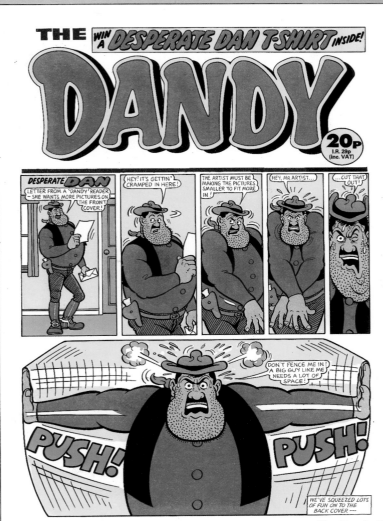

The Dandy October 24th, 1987.

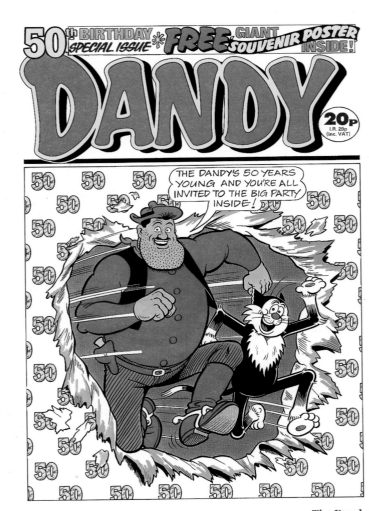

The Dandy December 5th, 1987.

As you can see, in the 1990's Dan is carrying on as strongly as ever.